EART~ ~~~ ~~~
CONQU

(Original Fren

co

by
Pierre Kohler

Translated from the French by
Albert V. Carozzi and Marguerite Carozzi

First English language edition published in 1988 by
Barron's Educational Series, Inc.

©1984 Hachette S.A., 79 boulevard Saint-Germain 75006 Paris

The title of the French edition is *La terre, l'univers et la conquete de l'espace.*

Library of Congress Catalog Card No. 87-33100

International Standard Book No. 0-8120-3831-2

BARRON'S

New York • London • Toronto • Sydney

Contents

PRINTED IN FRANCE

789   9687   987654321

A View From Space

Frank Borman, chief astronaut of the Apollo 8 mission, said that Earth is an oasis lost in the black desert of space. On the night before Christmas Eve, in 1968, he and his companions Jim Lovell and Bill Anders approached the moon, which no human being had ever flown over before. He then understood fully how truly beautiful our planet is. We can certainly share his enthusiasm while admiring the splendid picture taken at a distance of more than 100,000 kilometers (62,000 miles) by several Apollo missions (left picture).

This is probably how our planet has evolved *during 4.6 billion years: from a cloud of dust particles which drew closer together and joined to form a solid globe.*

Our Planet Earth

The Earth ranks third among other planets in distance from the sun but only fifth in size. Indeed, if Jupiter, the largest planet, were hollow it could contain 1,400 Earths! Hence, in comparison with several other planets in the solar system, the one we inhabit is very small. As far as its rank of third in distance, the Earth is 150 million kilometers (93,000,000 miles) from the sun. A simple calculation reveals that if the sun [1,400,000 kilometers in diameter (868,000 miles)] were a soccer ball, the Earth [12,742 kilometers in diameter (7,900 miles)] would represent a small pearl 70 meters away.

In terms of the human scale, however, the Earth is an enormous planet. Indeed, a distance of 40,000 kilometers (24,800 miles) must be traveled to go around it. With enough fuel, a commercial airplane would have to fly two days nonstop to travel the distance, but man-made satellites in low orbits take an hour and a half to circle the Earth.

Journey to the Center of the Earth

If, like the heroes of Jules Verne's famous novel, we could actually visit the center of the Earth, we would discover that the interior consists of several concentric "shells."

At the surface a thin layer of rocks forms the Earth's crust. Its thickness varies from only 5 kilometers (3 miles) under the oceans to 40 kilometers under mountain chains such as the Himalayas, the Alps, or the Andean Cordilleras. This crust consists essentially of granitic rocks.

Underneath the crust lies a mantle of basalt, a dark gray rock which is used for the construction of houses in some volcanic regions. Basalt is one of the main materials spewed out by volcanoes. The total thickness of the mantle is about 2,900 kilometers (1,800 miles).

The mantle surrounds an outer core of iron and nickel. This core is not very thick but its matter is much more packed or dense than elsewhere so that it alone comprises one third of the Earth's weight.

We should also be aware that temperature rapidly increases the deeper one penetrates the inner regions of our planet. At the bottom of a 5 kilometer (3 mile) deep well the temperature is already that of boiling water. In reality, Verne's imaginary journey would thus be unfeasible.

Because there is an atmosphere, *the surface of the Earth undergoes various forms of erosion (wind, rain) which modify the landscape. This picture shows the Grand Canyon in Arizona.*

The Earth is somewhat similar to a fruit with a central nucleus corresponding to a pit, a mantle to the pulp, and a crust representing the skin. The Earth's crust is very thin. The figures given on the cross-section are depths measured in kilometers from the surface.

The Planet "Ocean"

Seas and oceans cover 71%, that is nearly three quarters of the surface of the terrestrial globe. Our planet is the only one in the solar system where such great quantities of water can exist in liquid state. If the surface of the Earth were perfectly smooth, it would be covered with a uniformly deep, 2,900 meter (9500 feet) thick layer of ocean.

How Eratosthenes Measured the Earth

A little more than 200 B.C., the Greek scholar Eratosthenes noticed that at Syene (today Aswan), the sun at noon was exactly vertical on the first day of summer. However, in Alexandria, where he lived, obelisks cast shadows on the ground at the same time. After measuring the length of these shadows, he concluded that the sun was at an angle 7.2° from the vertical line. This angle represents the difference in latitude between Syene and Alexandria. Since 7.2° corresponds exactly to the 50th part of a circumference (7.2 x 50 = 360), it sufficed to multiply the distance between Syene and Alexandria (5,000 "stades" by 50 in order to obtain the circumference of the Earth. Knowing that a "stade," a length measurement used in the past, is 177.4 meters, the circumference therefore equals 5000 × 50 × 177.4 = 44,350 kilometers (27,500 miles). We know today that the polar circumference of Earth is 40,010 kilometers (24,800 miles), hence the dimensions of our planet were already known 2,200 years ago with only a 10% error.

Ethiopia, Somalia, and Saudi Arabia are *partially covered by clouds in this 1966 photograph taken by astronauts of the space capsule Gemini II, at an altitude of 1,300 kilometers (800 miles). Djibuti is located exactly at the strait that separates the Red Sea from the Gulf of Aden, an outlet of the Indian Ocean. The Red Sea has opened up slowly in the last 10 million years while Africa and Asia spread apart in the manner shown in the diagram at the top of the page.*

Movement of volcanic rocks on the seafloor (seafloor spreading).

Lava layers with south magnetic polarity (inverted).

Lava layers with north magnetic polarity (normal).

Fresh lava layers form submarine volcanoes

However, the surface of the Earth is not smooth at all. Mountains, plains, and valleys are found above sea-level (on continents) as well as on ocean floors.

Such a varied topography exists because the Earth's crust does not form an uninterrupted layer. Like a turtle's shell, it is formed by adjacent plates. However, the comparison ends here because on Earth we are dealing with plates of rock which move slowly against each other. This movement is extremely slow: only a few centimeters per year, yet it is important enough to change the face of the Earth profoundly during the course of geologic eras.

Forever Moving

South America and Africa were still lying side by side 125 million years ago, whereas North America and Europe drifted apart more recently, about 80 million years ago. The Atlantic Ocean, therefore, did not exist when dinosaurs began to inhabit the planet 225 millions years ago, but it had started to open when they disappeared about 65 million years ago.

Because of its continuing motion, our planet will be

completely different from what it is today in several dozen million years.

Thus, for the last 20 million years, a new ocean has been opening up in the Red Sea, a cut which extends southward through the great lakes of East Africa.

By contrast, the western part of the Mediterranean Sea between France and Algeria is closing up. California, on the other hand, is separating from North America and will form an island in the Pacific Ocean in 50 million years.

In Burma, this rock has mysteriously maintained equilibrium for centuries. Because of this astonishing property, it has been worshipped by the local inhabitants, who, by covering it with gold, designated it a sacred symbol.

This movement, called continental drift, was described in 1912 by the German meteorologist Alfred Wegener, but has been fully demonstrated by means of paleomagnetic, paleontologic, and paleoclimatic data only in the nineteen sixties.

Colliding with the South American plate, and plunging underneath it, the Pacific plate causes folding of the crust into mountains: the Andean Cordilleras.

South American continent
Andean Cordilleras
Bottom of the Pacific Ocean

The oceanic plate plunges underneath the continent

Folded mountains

Ashes

Lava

Magma

Magma erupting through the vent and the flanks of volcanoes is basalt, that is, molten rock.

Earthquakes and Volcanoes: Consequences of Continental Drift

Collision of continental plates causes buckling of continental crust, which results in mountain-building. When two oceanic plates converge, volcanic island arcs are generated. The collision of an oceanic plate with a continental plate causes volcanism and mountain-building (see figure of Andean Cordilleras). Finally, when two plates drift apart, upwelling of molten rock occurs, mainly in the form of submarine volcanoes (see picture, p.9). In other words, drifting of plates sometimes causes mountain-building and often causes volcanic eruptions and related earthquakes; in particular at the boundaries of plates. In fact, 80% of all volcanic activity is located around the Pacific Plate, thus forming the famous "circle of fire."

The two most destructive earthquakes in history occurred in China, in 1580 and in 1976. Together they killed 1,500,000 people. Other regions on Earth threatened by earthquakes are Japan, Indonesia, the Philippines, Iran, Turkey, Yugoslavia, Italy, North Africa, Central America, and Chile.

Volcanic eruption *on the island of Haimaey (Iceland) in 1973.*

On the surface of the Earth there exist about 500 active volcanoes which have had a total of more than 2,500 eruptions in the past. Some volcanoes form high mountains such as Aconcagua [7,000 meters (23,000 feet)] in the Andes or Mt. Erebus [3,800 meters (12,700 feet)] in Antarctica. The largest eruptions, which were also the most destructive, were those of Santorini, on the Island of Thera, in the Aegean Sea about 1460 A.D., and at Krakatoa, a small volcanic island in Indonesia's Sunda Islands, in 1883.

A Thin Layer of Air

The gaseous envelope surrounding the Earth constitutes the latter's atmosphere. It consists of two main gases: nitrogen (78%) and oxygen (21%); the remaining 1% includes various other gases, some of them present in very small amounts.

The pressure of this atmosphere, namely, the weight of the air above us, decreases rapidly the higher we are. Indeed, at an altitude of only 5,500 meters we have underneath us already half the volume of air present in the entire atmosphere.

The lower atmosphere, called troposphere, extends to an average altitude of 12 kilometers (7 miles) (a little less above the poles, a little more above the equator). Almost all meteorological phenomena occur in this part of the atmosphere. Above the troposphere is the stratosphere [up to 50 kilometers (30 miles)], where weather balloons operate;

White raindrops separate into seven colors, forming a rainbow, when crossing sunrays. The same phenomenon can be seen through a prism.

sunlight

raindrop

colors
of the rainbow

then the mesosphere [up to 80 kilometers (50 miles)], the thermosphere [up to 600 kilometers (372 miles)], and finally the exosphere where most man-made satellites are orbiting.

The atmosphere of the Earth has no well-defined limit. Its hazy boundary, which varies according to solar activity, is situated between an altitude of 3,000 and 3,500 kilometers (1,860 to 2,170 miles).

Astonishing Atmospheric Phenomena

Many spectacular light shows take place in the atmosphere. One of the best known is of course the rainbow. It forms when it rains in a portion of the sky in front of the observer while the sun is simultaneously behind him or her. When sun rays enter raindrops, light is broken up as in a prism into a grada-

Air rarefies rapidly with altitude. *It is difficult to breathe above 5 kilometers (3 miles). At an altitude of 17 kilometers (10 miles) where the Concorde flies, there is so little air that the sky is almost black at midday. Satellites above 120 kilometers (74 miles) orbit in a nearly complete vacuum.*

15

tion of colors ranging from blue to red and passing through green, yellow, and orange. All these colors are arranged in a semi-circle or an arc, and are reflected back to the observer.

When the sun or the moon are near the horizon, their rays have to cross an atmosphere which is about 30 times thicker than when they are at their zenith, which is high up in a vertical position. Their rays are, therefore, bent or refracted. As a result, the image of the sun or the moon appears flattened.

Often, the sun or moon appear to be larger when they are close to the horizon. This is an optical illusion due to the fact that in the sky we have no element of comparison whereas near the horizon, familiar objects (trees, houses, mountains, etc.) induce us into giving the moon and the sun greater relative proportions.

One may also wonder why the sky is blue. This color is caused by air molecules in the sky which mainly reflect rays of short wavelength (violet and blue) while absorbing most of the others. Conversely, when the layer of air is thicker (near the horizon) or polluted (saturated with dusts), rays of long wavelength (red and

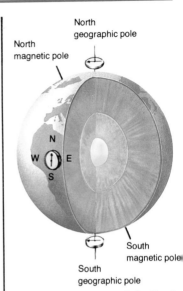

The axis of rotation of the Earth can be likened to a rod piercing the planet. The geographic poles are located at the places where the axis intersects the surface of the globe. The magnetic poles are displaced at an angle of about 10° from the geographic poles.

orange) are reflected, resulting in red color sunsets.

The Earth's Magnetic Field

Our planet has a magnetic field with a north and south pole. It is as if a gigantic magnet were located inside the Earth. Indeed, this "bar" always pulls the needle of a compass in the same direction and this fact lets us know where north is.

The places where the hypothetical bar pierces the surface of the Earth represent the magnetic poles. However, they do not coincide with the geographic poles, the ones shown on maps. They are, in fact, several thousand kilometers apart. The magnetic north pole is located in the Queen Elizabeth Islands in the Canadian Arctic Archipelago and the south pole is close to Adélie Land in Antarctica. Let us remember that the geographic poles correspond to the two end points of the axis of the Earth's rotation.

The Earth's magnetic field protects our planet *from solar charged particles. This invisible protective cocoon is formed by magnetic-field lines.*

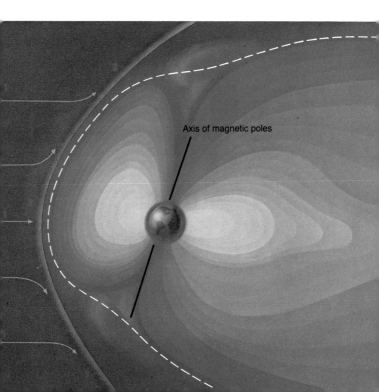

Axis of magnetic poles

The Solar System

One is generally not aware as to what extent the sun comprises the solar system. Every planet, their satellites—"moons" comparable to ours, and other bodies which we shall talk about, form a large circle of debris spread around the sun in a disk which is about 10 billion kilometers in diameter. The sun in the center represents 99.86% of all the matter in the solar system. Everything which surrounds it, including our beautiful Earth, is nothing but dust . . . .

Where did this system originate, how did it evolve?

Astronomers agree on the idea that our sun was created when a gigantic cloud of gases and dusts contracted some 4,600 million years ago. The stronger the contraction of this matter, the greater the increase of pressure at the center of the cloud. As a result, temperature increased enormously: up to 12 million degrees. At this temperature, some atoms joined others to form a single atom by fusion. Thus, hydrogen was changed into helium. This modification released

Mercury Venus Earth and moon Mars

an enormous amount of energy.

Thus a star began to shine: the sun was born.

Thereafter Distinct Bodies

The rotating sphere of matter which surrounded the sun at the beginning became flattened by the effect of centrifugal force. This matter acquired the shape of a disk. In its center, some sorts of lumps formed, sweeping each other up and enlarging by the snowball effect. When these bodies were sufficiently large, they took on an almost spherical shape and became planets.

Sweeping each other up, dust particles, which existed after the formation of the sun, produced spherical bodies of various sizes: the planets.

Jupiter   Saturn   Uranus   Neptune   Pluto

The Incas, like the Egyptians, worshipped the sun. At Machu Picchu, in the Peruvian Andes, stands a "solar stone" in front of which Inca priests used to greet the sunrise.

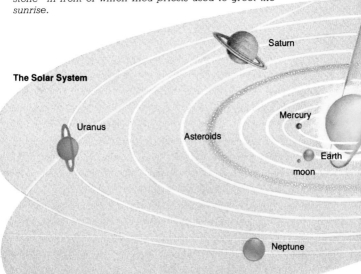

The Solar System

Saturn

Uranus

Asteroids

Mercury

Earth

moon

Neptune

Within a radius of 7 billion kilometers (46 billion miles) around the sun are found nine planets, about 50 moons, more than 3,000 asteroids, meteoroids, and comets.

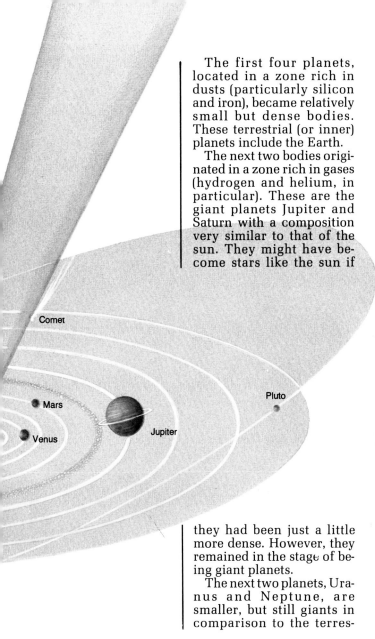

The first four planets, located in a zone rich in dusts (particularly silicon and iron), became relatively small but dense bodies. These terrestrial (or inner) planets include the Earth.

The next two bodies originated in a zone rich in gases (hydrogen and helium, in particular). These are the giant planets Jupiter and Saturn with a composition very similar to that of the sun. They might have become stars like the sun if

Comet

Mars

Venus

Jupiter

Pluto

they had been just a little more dense. However, they remained in the stage of being giant planets.

The next two planets, Uranus and Neptune, are smaller, but still giants in comparison to the terres-

The giant star Betelgeuse *is so large that part of the solar system extending to Mars could easily fit into it.*

trial planets. They consist essentially of ice because of the abundance of oxygen and hydrogen (constituents of water) and of the very low temperature [−180° to −220°C (−260 to −338°F)] of the remote regions of the solar system where they orbit.

Finally, there is Pluto, the smallest planet of the solar system. Not much is known about it except that it is covered by frozen methane. Methane is a gas composed of carbon and hydrogen which forms in the mud of swamps. It bubbles when a stick is thrust into the mud. Methane is also feared by miners because it may cause underground explosions. They call it by another name: firedamp.

What is the Difference between Stars and Planets?

Earth, Venus, Saturn, and the other planets, as well as their satellites such as the Moon, are relatively cold bodies which emit no light energy. They are apparently "dead" stars. By contrast, the Sun and the other stars are "living" stars in full evolution. We shall see that they are sites of powerful nuclear reactions which explain, among other things, their brightness.

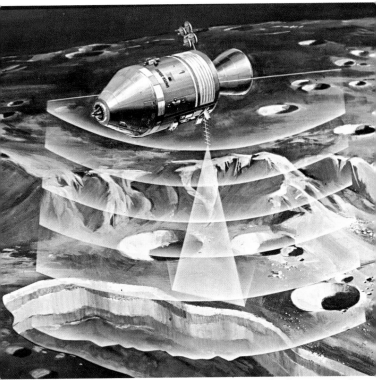

Detailed analysis of the surface of the moon by radar from an Apollo spacecraft.

A Gigantic Battlefield

Today, we are almost sure that the solar system was formed relatively fast. It was completed about 60 million years after the origin of the sun. With respect to its present age, these 60 million years are the equivalent of the first five months in a human life.

At the end of the cosmic "pool game" which gave birth to the planets, some smaller waste particles remained which continued to revolve about the sun. As a result of their random orbits, they bombarded the surfaces of various planets and their satellites. All show scars of these impacts, particularly those without an atmosphere.

The planets Mercury and Mars, especially, are riddled with craters. The same is true for virtually all the natural satellites of Mars, Jupiter, or Saturn.

Our own moon does not escape this rule as can be confirmed by simple examination of its surface with a telescope. Analyses carried out during the Apollo missions have shown that this cosmic bombardment was also of relatively short duration since it lasted "only" 600 to 700 million years.

The solar system has been quiet, therefore, for almost four billion years. Of course, some large meteorite impacts still occur from time to time but at a considerably lesser rate and intensity.

During the Apollo space program, from 1969 to 1972, twelve men walked on the moon. They discovered a dead and desert-like celestial body. As far as the eye can see, lunar lava plains are covered by a thin layer of dust and littered with stones of all sizes. Above the moon reigns an almost absolute vacuum. There is no air so that the sky is black even in the middle of the day. Scientific equipment left at the

Io, one of Jupiter's satellites (on the left), is about the size of the moon whose hidden face is partly shown here (on the right, top). Twelve men have already walked on the moon (on the right, below) whereas Io was merely flown over by automated spaceprobes.

surface by astronauts re-
vealed, among other things,
that quakes occur on the
moon. But they are of very
low intensity: the strongest
would be barely felt by man.

The moon's resources have
not yet been fully evaluated
in terms of their possible
exploitation. In spite of the
Challenger's tragic disaster,
further exploration of the
moon is being considered
again, but no precise date of
return to it has been established. Nevertheless, some
permanent scientific sta-
tions will certainly be in-
stalled similar to those in
Antarctica at the beginning
of the 20th century.

At any rate, men will not travel to other celestial bodies very soon because, although the duration of a spacetrip to the moon is only about a week, a roundtrip toward some nearby planets would involve years. Men, however, have never remained in space longer than 7 months. As for a spacetrip to the stars, with our present rockets it would last several thousand centuries!

For a long time to come, our knowledge of celestial bodies will have to be provided by automated spaceprobes or by space telescopes.

The exploration of the moon was carried out by automated spacecrafts (Soviet Lunokhod, left) and by astronauts who drove a specially designed jeep, called "moon rover" (American Apollo program, see below).

A Very Different "Twin": Venus

Earth is larger than the other terrestrial planets. Venus, however, is only barely smaller than Earth, and so astronomers considered it, not long ago, as Earth's twin. In reality, these two worlds differ in all respects.

Closer to the sun, Venus receives twice as much solar energy. Water, which it must have had earlier on, therefore evaporated and then dissociated under the action of the solar radiation. Ever since, the atmosphere of Venus has consisted of 96% carbon dioxide and 4% nitrogen.

Carbon dioxide has the same properties as glass in a greenhouse. It permits solar light to enter but retains heat reflected by the ground. Therefore, temperature rises up to +470°C (903°F). Metals such as lead or tin would melt at the surface of Venus. Furthermore, the atmospheric pressure on the ground is tremendous, 90 times that at the Earth's surface. The same pressure occurs in our oceans at a depth of 1 kilometer (half a mile).

Peculiar clouds float at an altitude of 42–59 kilometers (26–37 miles) above Venus. Instead of water vapor, as in terrestrial clouds, they contain droplets of sulfuric acid. They are so numerous and opaque that they form an unbroken cover.

It is therefore impossible to ever see the surface ground of Venus from Earth. Its topography could be determined only by radar observation. Radar waves can cross the clouds and permit us, so to speak, to "touch" Venus' ground surface from a distance. We know now that the surface has little relief with the exception of the Beta region, an area which might be the site of two still active volcanoes,

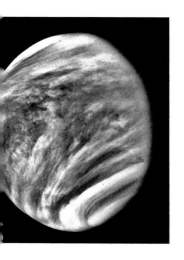

and the Alpha region with a ring-shaped feature, probably an ancient impact crater. Two plateaus, called Ishtar and Aphrodite, were also found.

Finally, at the border of the Ishtar plateau, at 65% latitude North, stands the highest mountain of Venus, Mount Maxwell which reaches the impressive elevation of 10,800 meters (36,000 feet).

To be visible, the clouds of Venus must be photographed through a blue filter (above). In reality, the surface of this planet is yellowish (below).

Mars, the Red Planet

Whereas Venus is closer to the sun than Earth, Mars is the fourth after Earth. Since it is farther away, it receives less energy from the sun so that, contrary to Venus, its temperature is very low, rarely reaching more than 0° C (32°F) at the surface. The average temperature is about −50°C (−58°F) and

Two great steps in space exploration: Landing of Viking spaceprobe on Mars in 1976 (below) and flying over the planets of Jupiter and Saturn by the Voyager spaceprobe between 1979 and 1981 (on the right).

−130° C was measured in the polar regions.

There is no longer any water on Mars. However, numerous sharply defined topographic features, in particular huge channel-like depressions which resemble meandering valleys, point to the former presence of water on this planet, and the possibilities that life might have existed in the past. According to geologists, presently water is probably buried underneath the ground of polar regions to form permafrost.

Pictures taken during several years by spaceprobes which landed on the surface of the planet show the development of seasons on Mars. They are almost twice as long as the terrestrial seasons; a Martian year equals, in fact 23 terrestrial months. It must be noted, however, that a day on Mars is as long as a day on Earth, the difference being only of a few minutes. Some snow showers were recorded in the winter but they were formed by dry ice, the main constituent of the Martian atmosphere (95%) being carbon dioxide.

The surface of Mars is completely desert and strewn with rocks of various shapes, sometimes rounded (resembling pumice), sometimes angular. These rocks are more or less buried beneath a carpet of reddish sand which contains a high proportion of iron oxide. At certain places, winds have formed small dunes.

Just as astonishing is the presence of enormous volcanoes in the northern hemisphere, on the Tharsis plateau. The largest among them, Nix Olympica, is a huge cone of lava with a diameter of 600 kilometers (372 miles) at its base and a height of 26,000 meters (that is three times as high as Mount Everest, the highest

And the "Little Green Men"?

In 1859, the Italian astronomer Secchi believed he had observed straight lines on Mars which he called "canali," or canals. Other observers confirmed his observations. Toward the end of the last century, more than 400 canals had been recorded! It was thought that only intelligent beings could have constructed them. Starting in 1898, the English writer H. G. Wells imagined in **The War of the Worlds** *how Martians invaded Earth. Thanks to spaceprobes, we know today that these alleged canals are, in fact, optical illusions. The Martians also are purely imaginary beings; there are no "little green men" on the red planet. Spaceprobes which landed on Mars found no sign of life.*

mountain on Earth!) It has been dormant for about 1 million years.

Analysis of the Martian soil made by automated spaceprobes showed no trace of life. Neither microbes, animals, nor plants exist at the surface of this desert-like planet.

Mercury: Torrid and Frozen

Mercury is the smallest terrestrial planet. It is only twice as big as our moon and resembles it like a sister. Indeed, spaceprobes which have flown over it showed that the surface is riddled with impact craters.

Mercury has no atmosphere. It is the closest planet to the sun. In its sky, the sun is three times larger than in ours. As a result, temperature is also higher and reaches almost 400°C (750°F) at noon at the equator. Inversely, since no atmosphere is storing heat, temperature drops at night below −150°C (−212°F).

Mercury is thus the planet with the largest variation in temperature in half a day [about 600°C (1140°F)]. Note that half a day on Mercury corresponds to nearly three months on Earth.

Mercury looks very much like the moon. *Very close to the sun, this planet experiences a temperature of +400° C (750° F) on its day side. However, since there is no air to distribute heat, temperature drops to −150° C (−212° F) on its night side.*

The Countless Asteroids

Moving away from the sun, beyond Mars, thousands of small planets revolve in a huge belt 500 million kilometers (310 million miles) wide. These are the asteroids, the largest of which, Ceres [785 kilometers (490 miles)], was discovered in 1801. Others were discovered since that time and more than 2600 can be counted today, about one new one being added each day. Those which were photographed with modern equipment have a diameter of only a few hundred meters; nevertheless, smaller ones certainly exist as well.

If all known asteroids were melted together into a single body, it would form a globe only 1,500 kilometers (930 miles) in diameter, 600 times less voluminous than Earth.

Giant Planets

Jupiter and Saturn are the two largest planets in the solar system. These enormous spheres of gases are surrounded by a thin atmosphere which includes clouds of methane and of ammonia crystals. These clouds extend in alternating light and dark bands parallel to the equator due to the intense centrifugal force caused by the rotation of these planets. Jupiter and Saturn rotate, in fact, very rapidly around their axis in about 10 hours. At the equator, cloud speeds of 500 kilometers (310 miles) per hour and 1,800 kilometers (1,110 miles) per hour for Saturn were recorded.

Between Mars and Jupiter revolve asteroids: thousands of stony bodies, most of which are only a few kilometers in diameter.

34

Photographs by Voyager space-probes show details of the cloudy bands of Jupiter (above). Beneath these clouds, the planet is an enormous ball consisting of several layers of helium and hydrogen (on the right). A thin ring of matter was also discovered around the planet.

Our storms on these giant planets would thus be felt as gentle breezes.

In the middle of the clouds of Jupiter, temperature is close to −140°C (−194°F). The most unusual atmospheric feature of this planet is a sort of enormous reddish "eye" called the Great Red Spot. Its size decreases slowly but the spot nevertheless is about 40,000 kilometers (25,000 miles) long.

No giant red spot exists on Saturn but white spots were observed: they are extremely violent cyclones.

And Comets?

A brightly shining head with a long luminous tail becoming larger and larger because it is more and more lighted when approaching the sun: this is the rare but grandiose show offered by comets when they come close to Earth (see figure below). No direct observation of their solid parts has been made. We are certain they consist of a core of ice nulcei and dusts. Comets have very elongated orbits that extend far out to several tens of billions of kilometers, indeed to the limits of the solar system; some comets extend even beyond the planetary orbits. Today, scientists think that some comets came from outside the solar system and entered it for the first time when they were observed.

Rings of Ice-Blocks

Saturn's rings have been observed for a long time. Galileo discovered them in 1610 when he looked at this planet for the first time with a telescope. He did not know, however, what they were. The Dutch astronomer Christian Huygens found the right explanation forty years later.

The rings of Saturn are nothing else but thousands and thousands of ice-blocks

Saturn's rings consist of closely-spaced rotating ice-blocks.

which revolve, in closely spaced rings, around the planet in a disk some 300,000 kilometers (185,000 miles) in diameter. This disk is, however, very flat since it is less than 100 meters (350 feet) thick. On the same scale, an L.P. record would have a diameter of 30 kilometers (19 miles)! If the ice forming the rings of Saturn were melted to form a single body, it would represent a globe of only 300–350 kilometers (190–220 miles) in diameter.

The "Last Born"

Whereas the above-mentioned planets are visible with the naked eye and were therefore known since long ago, the icy giants, Uranus and Neptune, were added to the list of planets by astronomers only very recently. Uranus was discovered in 1781 by the British astronomer William Herschel and Neptune in 1846 by the German observer Jean Galle.

These planets are so far away [2.6 to 4.3 billion

kilometers (1.5 to 2.5 billion miles) from Earth respectively] that the most powerful telescopes show us only some vague gray streaks at their surface. We know only that they are surrounded by a thick atmosphere of methane and that the axis of rotation of Uranus is nearly level with its orbital plane. In other words, this planet revolves almost completely recumbent (lying down). This unusual situation was possibly caused by the collision with an Earth-size body. In 1977, nine rings were discovered around Uranus; these rings are thin and dark. Uranus has five known satellites, whereas Neptune has two.

Pluto, the latest planet of the solar system to be discovered, was found in 1930 by the American astronomer Clyde Tombaugh. It is the smallest planet with a diameter of only about 3,000 kilometers (2000 miles).

The Sun: An Ordinary Star

Compared to the sun, planets are very small; terrestrial planets and Pluto are even smaller. Yet the sun is not an extraordinary star in comparison to many other stars (remember that the sun itself is a star). Indeed, it appears pathetically small when compared to one of

An Extraordinary Speed

Light travels at the extraordinary speed of 300,000 kilometers (185,000 miles) per second, 1 billion kilometers (600,000,000 miles) per hour, and 10,000 billion kilometers (6,200 billion miles) per year. The distance traveled by light in a year represents a unit measure, the light-year, with which the enormous distances between the stars and the stellar systems, the galaxies, are measured. Furthermore, astronomers use the parsec which is about 3.26 light-years.

the largest known stars such as VV Cephei which is, in fact, 2 billion times larger than the sun.

However, although nearly a "dwarf," with its diameter of 1,400,000 kilometers (900,000 miles), the sun is nevertheless large enough that it could contain more than a million planets the size of Earth!

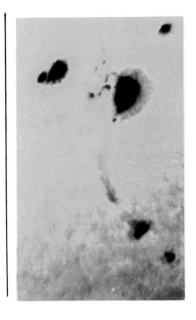

At the surface of the sun are dark spots with jagged edges (above). A vast and hot atmosphere extends above the surface and is invisible in the blue sky: the corona (below). Pictures taken by astronomical satellites permit us to visualize the corona.

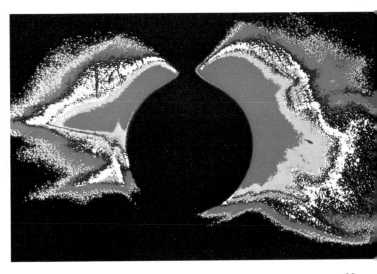

Revealing Spots

What we see of the sun in the sky corresponds only to the envelope from which the solar radiation escapes and to which our eye is sensitive. This envelope is the so-called photosphere.

On the photosphere can be seen "rice grains," generally called granulation, which are a juxtaposition of small spots about 2,000 kilometers (1,240 miles) in diameter which correspond to bubbles of hot gases (hotspots). More impressive are the dark spots (sunspots) with jagged edges which are scattered over the solar disk.

They correspond to zones where the internal magnetic field of the sun breaks through the surface and causes cooling. Whereas the average temperature of the photosphere is about 5,500°C

The "flames" of the sun (prominences) are hydrogen surges.

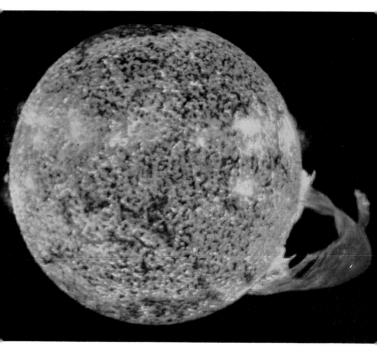

The sun was long considered a God. This Egyptian bas-relief represents the pharaoh Akhnaton worshipping the sun which was more important than all other gods.

(9,950°F), it is only 4,000°C (7,250°F) near the spots. Thus, they appear black in contrast with their surroundings.

A record-breaking group of 107 sunspots extended over 320,000 kilometers (200,000 miles) in April 1947. In front of this group, the Earth could have been aligned 25 times. On the average, an isolated large spot or a small group equals the size of our planet. These sunspots disappear after a few weeks and are replaced by new ones.

After recording the sunspots' daily positions scientists were able to measure the time of rotation of the sun. Since the sun consists of a fluid mass, it rotates faster at the equator than in the polar regions: 25 and 34 days, respectively. The number and extent of sunspots varies in cycles of about 11 years. This is the cycle of solar activity.

Huge Hydrogen Arches

Above the photosphere extends a 10,000 kilometer (6200 mile) thick gaseous layer. This is the chromosphere which corresponds to the lower atmosphere of the sun. Prominences, which are a type of solar flames, do not represent a process of combustion as we know it on Earth. They originate in the chromosphere. These prominences are gigantic arches of hydrogen which surge up to an elevation of several tens of thousands of kilometers, become deformed, shatter, and fall back toward the sur-

face in a few hours. In 1946, during a peak of activity of the solar cycle, one prominence was observed to reach 1,700,000 kilometers (over 1,000,000 miles) which is more than the diameter of the sun itself.

Above the chromosphere is the corona, which is the upper atmosphere of the

Corona

Prominence

The interior of the sun consists of hydrogen at a temperature of several million degrees which forms eddies called convection currents. These currents carry hot gases from the interior to the surface of the sun.

sun. It is visible to us only during total solar eclipses because its brightness is 1 million times lower than that of the blue sky. Therefore, it cannot normally be seen except with the help of special instruments called coronagraphs which enable us to recreate artificial eclipses.

Energy Spent but Also Great Reserves Left

It is quite difficult to know what lies underneath the visible surface of the sun because direct observations are impossible. Extremely powerful nuclear reactions from which the sun gains its energy occur here. Every

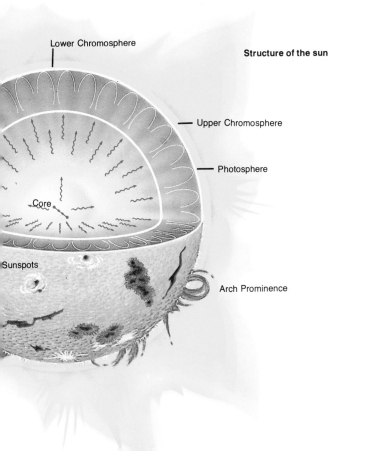

Structure of the sun

Lower Chromosphere

Upper Chromosphere

Photosphere

Core

Sunspots

Arch Prominence

second, 600 million tons of hydrogen are transformed into 596 million tons of helium. The difference, namely 4 million tons, is instantly transformed into energy. In order to shine, the sun loses 345 billion tons of gases daily; however, this represents a mere droplet compared to its total mass. In fact, since its origin, the sun has only lost 0.03% of its original matter. At this rate, astronomers forecast the sun's future life span to be 5–7 billion years.

Let us remember that the sun is an insignificant star of modest size. It is only one among many of a large family of various stars.

Stars vary in size. As mentioned earlier, VV Cephei is monstrous in size compared to the sun. Nevertheless,

Other Auroras

The chromosphere appears to be "angry" at times. Solar eruptions occur. These are flares of charged particles full of energy. They surge far into space. When they reach the Earth, they cause various phenomena. For instance, they interfere with long distance radio communications. They also act upon the movements of the atmosphere and may change weather conditions. Particularly impressive are beautiful polar auroras caused by solar eruptions which can be seen both in the north (auroras borealis) and in the south (auroras australis). These are large luminous arches in the sky which are caused by the collision of solar particles and the upper layers of the atmosphere at the poles.

To compensate for defects of lenses, *the astronomer Johannes Hevelius built this 40 meter (130 feet) long tubeless telescope in 1670.*

smaller stars do exist. For instance, Sirius B is only about the size of the Earth. Even smaller stars such as pulsars were discovered. Their diameter is only a few tens of kilometers, which is barely the size of a large city. However, size is not the principal criterion for the classification of stars. We shall discuss them in more detail below.

A Question of Colors

Stars are classified by astronomers according to their spectral type, that is their color, which itself is due to their surface temperature.

Streaks of Fire in the Sky

Shooting stars (meteoroids), in spite of their name, are not stars falling from the sky. In reality, they consist of small stony and metallic particles which revolve around the Sun and sometimes cross the orbit of the Earth. When they cross the atmosphere at great speed [sometimes at 250,000 kilometers (155,000 miles) per hour!], they melt and vaporize in a fraction of a second and produce a transient and silent fiery streak across the sky.

Do stars have different colors? The answer is truly surprising given that they all appear white when we see them at night. In fact, our eyes do not function well in darkness and can barely distinguish any colors. However, the sky differs completely when seen through a telescope.

Indeed, among the many stars, one notices blue, green, yellow, orange, and red ones. The blue ones are the hottest [more than 30,000°C (54,000°F) at the surface] and the red ones are the coldest [3,000°C (5,500°F) "only"]. The sun is a yellow star with a temperature in the photosphere of about 5,000°C (9,000°F) as mentioned above.

Variable stars exist with varying degrees of brightness, lasting from a few hours to several dozens of years.

When a star moves away or approaches us, *its spectral lines, which correspond to the colors of the rainbow, shift toward the red or the blue, respectively.*

The following double page: *the sky as it appears at the North Pole, the South Pole, and at the equator. The solar path (map of the equator) are charted based on the fact that the sun's and the Earth's axes are not parallel (they form an angle of ca. 23°). During its annual path, the sun crosses the constellations of the Zodiac.*

Star Chart of the North Polar Hemisphere

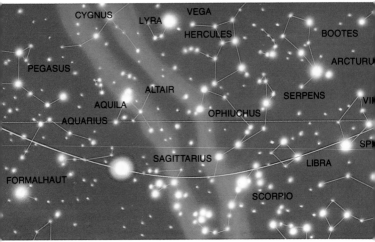

48

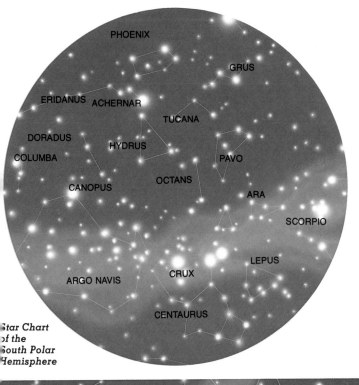

**Star Chart
of the
South Polar
Hemisphere**

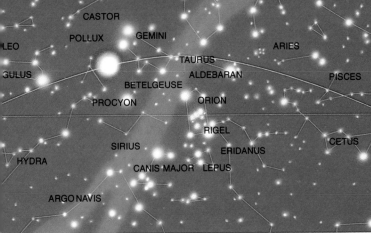

Star Chart of the Celestial Equator *(from left to right and from top to bottom):*

The Milky Way

On a dark night, it is possible to see among the stars a long whitish streak called the Milky Way. It is formed by numerous stars too closely packed to be distinguished individually. Best seen on September evenings, the Milky Way stretches from the northeastern to the southwestern horizon and passes through the zenith. Half-way across, it divides into two branches. The right branch is sparse. The left branch, in the constellation of Sagittarius, is particularly dense, however, and it is here that the center of our Galaxy is located.

A galaxy is some sort of a gigantic stellar city in which stars represent buildings. The same holds for our Galaxy (written with a capital G in order to distinguish it from other galaxies). The Milky Way represents the "downtown" of this stellar city and we see it from the suburbs because the sun is located at the edge of the Galaxy.

In profile, our Galaxy looks like a flattened disk with a bulging center; from the front, it resembles a "sun" of fireworks. Its diameter is about 100,000 light-years and its thickness 15,000 light-years.

The sun is located 30,000 light-years from the Galaxy's center, around which it revolves (as do all other stars) in 220 million years. Since its birth, the sun has already accomplished about twenty revolutions.

Astronomers estimate the number of stars in our Galaxy to be close to 200 billion. On a clear night, about 2,500 of them are visible to the naked eye.

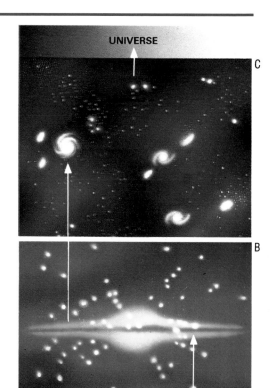

UNIVERSE

C

B

A

Earth is only one planet *among many in the solar system (A). The solar system, with the sun at its center, is located at the edge of a large disk which includes 200 billion other stars: the Galaxy (B). This Galaxy in turn is part of a group of some thirty galaxies: the Local Cluster (C), itself lost in the universe.*

Open Clusters

Stars are thus very numerous in the Galaxy. But since they extend over such vast areas, the average distance between individual stars is very great. The closest star, Proxima Centauri, is a little over 4 light-years away from us. The second closest, Barnard's star, is 6 light-years away. Only eight stars are found in a radius of 10 light-years around the sun. On the average, these stars are separated from each other by a distance which is about 10 million times their diameter. Proportionally, this is

Constellations and the Zodiac

In order to orient themselves better with the sky, astronomers, since long ago, visualized imaginary lines between the brightest stars, supposedly showing animals or mythological heroes. Thus, we find, for instance, Lion (LEO), Swan (CYGNUS), Eagle (AQUILA), HERCULES, and PERSEUS. A first set of 48 constellations were described by Ptolemy in 137 A.D. During the following centuries, many other astronomers completed this cartography and eventually extended it to the southern hemisphere.

Finally in 1927, the International Astronomical Union published the configurations of 88 constellations. Twelve of these constellations are crossed by the sun during its annual path and make up the Zodiac. These are AQUARIUS (January 21), PISCES (February 20), ARIES (March 21), TAURUS (April 21), GEMINI (May 22), CANCER (June 22), LEO (July 23), VIRGO (August 23), LIBRA (September 23), SCORPIO (October 23), SAGITTARIUS (November 22), and CAPRICORN (December 21).

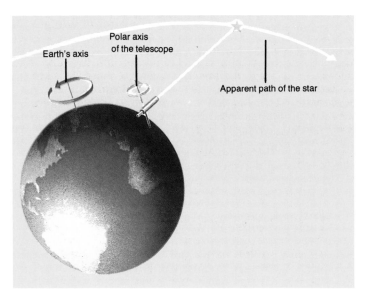

Earth's axis

Polar axis of the telescope

Apparent path of the star

To compensate for the rotation of the Earth, *telescopes must turn in the opposite direction (above). Large stone sundials at Jaipur, India (below), built in the 18th century, give time according to the sun's position.*

like pinheads spaced out every 20 kilometers (12 miles).

However, stars are also grouped in clusters in the Galaxy. Some are called "open" clusters because they are loose groups of tens or hundreds of stars that are rather distant from each other. The most beautiful open cluster is the Pleiades in the constellation Taurus.

Globular Clusters

More spectacular than open clusters are globular clusters which include up to 100,000 stars grouped in a ball 150 light-years in diameter.

The nearest globular cluster NGC 6397 is nevertheless at the considerable distance of 8,000 light-years from the sun. It is noteworthy, indeed, that globular clusters surround our Galaxy like some kind of halo and thus form its boundaries.

The most beautiful globular cluster is Omega in the constellation Centaurus. It is visible only in the Southern hemisphere.

What Reference Numbers are Used in Astronomy?

In order to classify stars and galaxies, astronomers have established various catalogs. Stars are named by the initials of the chosen catalog, followed by a number. Thus, the Andromeda galaxy is sometimes called M31 because it is the 31st celestial body catalogued at the end of the 18th century by the French astronomer Charles Messier. However, the same galaxy is also called NGC 224 by American astronomers according to Dreyer's **New General Catalogue** *(1888).*

The North America Nebula, in the constellation of Cygnus, resembles our continent.

The Astonishing Nebulae

The Galaxy is not simply a large collection of stars but it also contains clouds of interstellar dust and gases. Some astronomers believe these clouds stem either from residues of exploded stars or from residues abandoned after the formation of some stars, but others consider them to be distant galaxies.

When these clouds are near an active star, they become "excited" by its radiation and start to shine. One then notices in the sky some beautifully colored arrangements which form diffuse nebulae. The most spectacular is certainly the great Orion nebula.

Finally, let us mention planetary nebulae, thus named because they often assume the form of a planet. They are gaseous envelopes ejected by certain stars during growth crises.

The great Orion nebula, mapped by a radiotelescope (green lines), does not have the same shape as in pictures taken through a regular telescope.

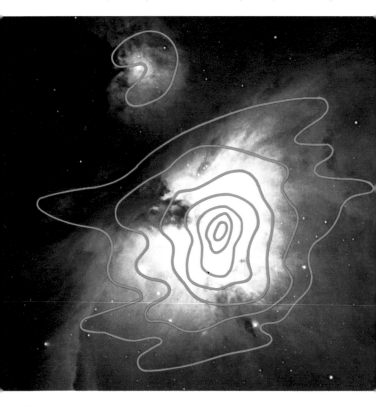

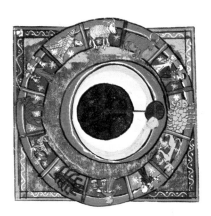

The Signs of the Zodiac. *Manuscript of the 15th century.*

 ### *Should We Believe in Horoscopes?*

*Many newspapers publish horoscopes forecasting
the fate of an individual according to the position
of the stars at the time of birth.
Since earliest times, the people of Mesopotamia,
Egypt, and Greece believed that the future could
be read in the stars. Thus, astrology was born.
However, because constellations are purely imaginary figures and because it is evident that in-
dividuals born at the same time all over the world
cannot have the same fate, the foundations of
astrology are not accurate. (Astrology should not
be confused with astronomy, which is a science
based on actual observation.)*

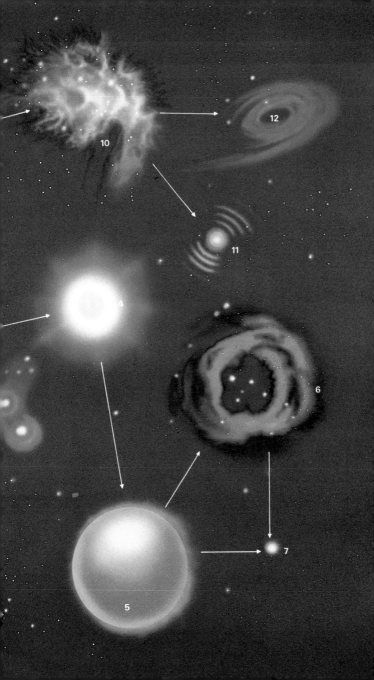

Preceding double page:
Depending on whether they have more or less gas than the sun, *the stars have very different fates. After the period called T Tauri (2) where they assume their spherical shape from a cloud of hydrogen (1), they start to shine as does the sun today (4); the younger stars such as the Pleiades (3) remain surrounded by layers of nonabsorbed gas. A small star such as our sun ages slowly (10 billion years) before becoming a red giant (5 and 6) and then a white dwarf (7). The larger stars turn into blue giants (8) which rapidly consume their hydrogen (in less than 1 billion years) and then explode into supernovas (9); the gas released during this process will feed new nebulae while the center of the star collapses into a pulsar (10) or a black hole (11).*

The sky *as it must appear from the surface of a planet which revolves around a neighboring star.*

The Fate of Stars

Stars are not stationary celestial bodies even though their life is usually recorded over billions of years. They are born, evolve, and die, a little like human beings. Their fate depends mostly upon one criterion: their original size.

The smallest live for a long time (more than 10 billion years). On the contrary, the largest disappear in only a few million years after having exhausted all their energy reserves. They often die in an explosion and form supernovas.

Neither too small, nor too large, the sun has and will continue to have a relatively calm life. At present, it is near the middle of its life cycle and according to astronomers, it will last another 5–7 billion years.

Towards its end, the sun will expand and engulf the first four planets, from Mercury to Mars. The surface of the Earth will be burned to ashes. Thereafter, the sun will contract and become a white dwarf, namely a degenerated star, no larger than Earth, and should remain in that state as long as the universe lasts.

Strange Skeletons: Pulsars

If the initial mass of the star is at least one third greater than that of the sun, the star's evolution is different. For instance, if the quantity of initial hydrogen is twice that of the sun, the star will live only 1 billion years, that is ten times less than the sun. It will explode and become a supernova.

The brightness of the explosion is of such intensity

that the star becomes visible from Earth, even in the middle of the day, because its brightness is like that of a billion combined suns! Nevertheless, such phenomena are extremely rare and only nine explosions of supernovas have been recorded since the beginning of the Christian era, the most recent in 1987.

After the explosion, stellar material is blown into space at a speed of up to several million kilometers per hour. However, at the center of the supernova, an extraordinarily dense core subsists which rotates at a tremendous speed, namely

Black Holes are supposed to be some sort of holes in space which engulf nearby stellar gases.

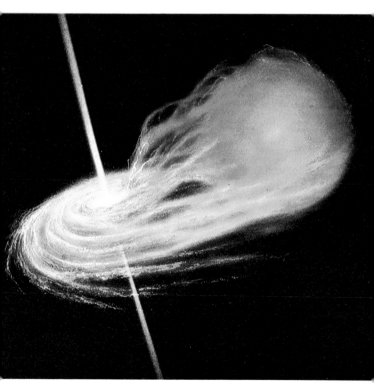

several rotations per second, whereas the sun takes almost a month for one rotation. Radiation emitted by this dense core sweeps through space like some haphazard beacon.

These astonishing stars are called pulsars. The matter of which they are formed is so compact that their density is 100,000 billion times greater than that of the sun. A small particle of a pulsar, the size of a pinhead, would weigh on a terrestrial scale the incredible amount of 400,000 tons or the equivalent of 10,000 railroad cars!

Cannibals Among Stars

Astronomers imagine even more extraordinary fates for stars whose initial hydrogen mass was 3–4 times greater than that of the sun.

After exploding into a supernova, the density of its center is supposedly so great that the pulsar collapses under its own weight.

Avicenna, Arab philosopher in 1,000 A.D., recorded the position of stars.

63

Neutrons, which are the atomic particles that form it, behave like eggs that are being continuously piled up. After some time the eggs at the bottom are crushed by the weight of those above them. In the case of a star, an implosion occurs, namely an explosion in reverse directed toward the center.

The initial matter contracts further and occupies an increasingly smaller space while its density infinitely grows. A time comes when the force of attraction of this small star is such that even photons, that are like grains of light, cannot escape anymore. They become prisoners of this extraordinary star which absorbs its own light and thus becomes visible.

Similar to a hole, it engulfs all matter, hence its name of **black hole.**

Galaxies of the Local Cluster

Just as the sun is only one star lost among 200 billions in the Milky Way, our Galaxy is merely one galaxy among billions of others.

Dwarf galaxies exist which contain "only" 10 billion stars whereas giant galaxies include up to 1,000 billion stars! The shape of galaxies varies also; they may be lenticular, elliptical, spiral, barred spiral, or irregular.

Galaxies are not distributed in an orderly fashion in the Universe. Indeed, they are generally assembled in groups or clusters. These galactic groups form, in turn, "supergroups." Our own Galaxy belongs to a small cluster, the local cluster, which includes thirty other clusters.

This local cluster is essentially dominated by two large galaxies: ours and the Andromeda galaxy (M31, or NGC224). The Andromeda galaxy is the only one of its

The most distant stars are quasars which represent cores of primitive galaxies. They are as big as a large star but release as much energy as several billion stars put together. The nearest ones are more than 2 billion light-years from Earth.

kind we can see with the naked eye in the northern hemisphere. It forms a small hazy spot in the constellation of the same name. Our Galaxy, together with the Andromeda galaxy, includes three fourths of the 300 billion stars from the 28 galaxies listed in the local group.

Much larger groups of galaxies exist elsewhere in the universe. The most important cluster is certainly the Virgo galaxy, also called Virgo group, which is 45 million light-years away from us. This group includes 3,000 galaxies, a hundred times more than the local group.

Our Galaxy has a spiral shape. *Other galaxies have different shapes: for instance, elliptical or lenticular.*

At The Frontiers Of The Universe

The closest of the large galaxies is 2,250,000 light-years away from Earth. The only exceptions are the Magellanic Clouds—two very small irregular galaxies, which are satellites of our own Galaxy. This is the Andromeda galaxy (M31 or NGC224). It is also the most distant star visible to the naked eye: 21 billion kilometers (13 billion miles) away! The galaxies of the Virgo group are 45 million light-years away, whereas there are others at even greater distances. Photographs taken with the most powerful telescopes show galaxies at a distance close to a billion light-years away.

At the frontiers of the universe, bodies of another nature were observed. At first, they were thought to be stars. However, they were found to release an extraordinary amount of energy which is equivalent to that of several billion stars put together. They were named quasars, a contraction of the expression "quasistars."

The resolution of our view of the universe depends above all upon two factors: the diameter of the mirror of telescopes and the sensitivity of photographic plates or of the electronic camera placed at the focal point of these telescopes. The larger the mirror, the more light is concentrated at the focal point where observation is taking place. Furthermore, a device is necessary to register the pale lights of distant stars which our eye could never perceive directly.

Toward the end of 1986, the giant Hubble space tele-

The great Andromeda galaxy is one of the nearest galaxies. Its central part, which is filled with stars, is sufficiently bright to be seen with the naked eye as a hazy star when the sky is very dark.

This is the Challenger space shuttle which was programmed to put in orbit, at an altitude of 500 kilometers (310 miles), a large space telescope, 240 cm (8 feet) in diameter. It was to revolutionize astronomical observations in 1986. Due to the tragic Challenger explosion, the program was postponed.

Jettison of booster rockets

Separation of main fuel tank and insertion of shuttle into orbit

Take-off from Cape Canaveral launching pad

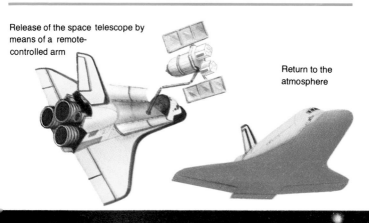

Release of the space telescope by means of a remote-controlled arm

Return to the atmosphere

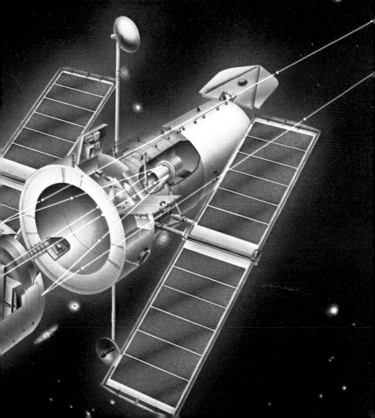

scope was going to be put into orbit by the Challenger space shuttle at an altitude of 500 kilometers (310 miles) from Earth. It was programmed to gather information from the frontiers of the universe. Because of the tragic Challenger explosion, however, the program was delayed several years.

These were the objectives: aided by a completely black sky in space, beyond the screen created by the atmosphere, the telescope was to discover stars 100 times less bright than the most distant ones visible today. In other words, astronomers would have been able to see ten times farther away.

What did we hope to find? It is difficult to know, particularly since the theoretical limit of the universe is placed at less than 20 billion light-years, whereas a space telescope should have been able to gather information from a distance of about 100 billion light-years away! As a matter of fact, we should have been able to see, if not the birth of the universe, at least what happened immediately afterwards.

Sally Ride, who has flown in space twice and was a member of the commission that investigated the explosion of the Challenger, proposed the following space goals. 1. Exploration of planet Earth from space between the years 1996 and 2000. 2. Robotic exploration of the solar system including missions to Saturn and Mars beginning in 1996. 3. Exploration of the moon for potential resources and for the investigation of the possibility of extracting oxygen from lunar soil. Installation of an outpost with housing, research facilities, and a rover vehicle by the year 2005. 4. Landing of astronauts on Mars with the establishment of an outpost there in the 21st century.

Once our space telescope is placed in orbit, the question will be asked: what shall we see? This involves a number of factors concerning time.

Older and Older

Man's beliefs about his place in the Universe as well as about its dimensions and age have changed drastically since long ago. We know today that neither the Earth—as was believed in the Middle Ages—nor the sun are the center of the world. We know also that our Galaxy is only a tiny part of the vast universe.

With respect to our notion of the age of the universe, it is striking to notice that it has considerably increased in the last centuries, and even in the last decades.

The first precise date was given in 1658 by the Irish Archbishop James Usher who, after studying the Bible, decided that the world originated in 4,000 B.C.

Paleontological discoveries during the past century then pushed back the age of the Earth to 2 billion years.

Thereafter, geologists came to the conclusion that the Earth was about 4.5 billion years old. Since our planet could not be older than the universe itself, it was necessary to reconsider earlier estimates of the age of the universe. More precise measurements of the speed at which galaxies move, calculated after 1960, allowed scientists to establish the origin of the universe approximately at 15 billion years ago, with a margin of error of + or − 5 billion years. This shows how great our uncertainties still are.

Hieronymus Bosch painted this biblical paradise on Earth in the 15th Century. All religions have their ideas about the origin of the universe and their comparative study is of great interest for the history of astronomy.

71

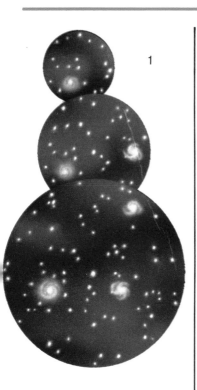

continuously in space at a rate which compensates exactly for the thinning of matter by expansion. The universe is infinite in space and time and had neither a beginning nor an end.

2. The theory of the expanding universe, born from the explosion of a small initial core, named the big-bang theory, was proposed in 1927 by the Belgian astronomer Abbé Georges Lemaître.

At the Beginning: the Big Bang!

Modern theories on the origin of the universe are only half a century old and are divided into two groups.

1. The theory of a static (or steady-state) universe was proposed by the British astronomers Fred Hoyle, Thomas Gold, and Hermann Bondi in 1948. According to that theory, the universe is being created

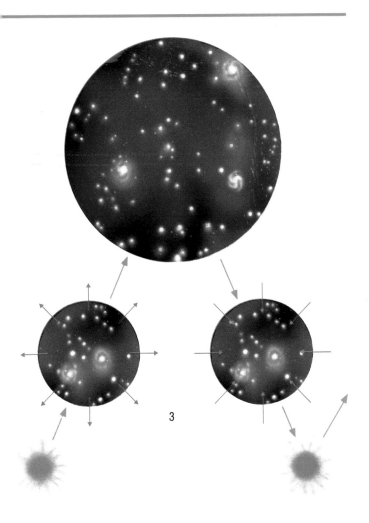

3

Three Hypotheses *try to explain the origin and the evolution of the universe. 1. The steady-state theory proposes a universe which is being created continuously. It has always existed and will never end (left). 2. The expanding universe, born during an initial explosion, the big bang (center). 3. The pulsating universe which expands, contracts, and explodes in cycles (above).*

The phenomenon of the receding galaxies and the discovery in 1965 of cosmic background radiation, supposedly a remnant of the original explosion, contributed to a shift in favor of the big-bang theory and to its acceptance by the majority of astronomers.

The universe would thus resemble a balloon which is being inflated, at the surface of which are glued confetti representing galaxies. With increasing expansion, the confetti become more and more distant from each other. Indeed, this observation holds for galaxies. Their interior corresponds to the past (namely, to the site where the balloon was an instant before) whereas their exterior represents the future (namely, the position it will occupy later on). The radius of the balloon is thus comparable to the time dimension which is one-way, from the past to the future.

Imagine some kind of pony express from New Orleans to St. Louis. A mailman would be collecting letters all along the way. At his arrival in St. Louis, the recipient would receive fairly recent news from his friend in Memphis, a little older ones from his correspondent in Jackson, and the oldest from his correspondent in New Orleans.

The same holds for the universe where the messenger carrying news about the stars (light) does not travel at an infinite speed. Indeed, we see the moon as it was a little over a second ago (because its distance is just a little greater than a light-second), the sun as it was eight minutes earlier, Saturn as it was 1½ hour earlier, and so forth.

We must also know that when the light of the polar star reaches our eye, it has already traveled for five centuries. Furthermore, the light of the Andromeda galaxy left it two million years ago, at a time when our distant ancestors, Australopithecus, lived. Light from the most distant quasar has traveled 13 billion years when it arrives on Earth. It thus left when neither the Earth nor the sun existed.

What is the Future of the Universe?

Astronomers hold different views on this subject. Two possibilities exist which both appear plausible considering the state of our present knowledge.

The universe is either expanding indefinitely, that is

expanding without ever stopping, or its expansion will slow down and stop after having reached a certain volume, and it will start contracting until it reaches the supercontracted state it had before the big bang.

In the first case, the universe is said to be "open," in the second it is "closed." There is, in fact, another alternative or third theory: the pulsating universe which after having reached its initial state, undergoes another explosion, followed by another contraction, and so on in a never-ending cycle.

The space telescope might permit us to give an answer to this question in the future.

Is Mankind Alone in the Universe?

Spaceprobes which have flown over various planets of the solar system and have

Authors of science-fiction such as Pierre Boulle in "The Planet of the Apes," have visualized travels at the speed of light.

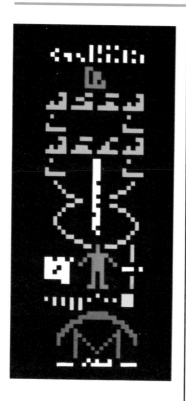

landed on some of them showed that organized life does not exist anywhere except on Earth. Nevertheless, we cannot refrain from imagining the existence of living beings on some planet revolving around other stars.

For the time being, however, we have no way of knowing about these planets directly (whereas it might be possible to do so with the space telescope), nor to discover life from a distance unless civilizations similar to ours exist on some of these planets and are capable of sending radio messages into space.

This is why the American scientist Frank Drake started Project OZMA, the first search with a radio telescope turned toward some nearby stars, similar to the

Messages were sent into space: *in 1974 (left) a radio message was sent which, once decoded, shows this configuration in which the figure of a human being living on Earth is portrayed, as well as formulas for DNA, numbers, atomic numbers, and representations of the solar system. In 1973 (right), this engraved plaque was attached to the Pioneer 10 spacecraft. One recognizes a couple from Earth as well as a diagram of the solar system. Pioneer 10 left the solar system in June 1983.*

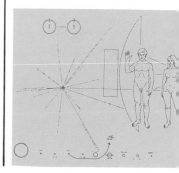

in, hoping to receive some "intelligent" messages. After this first experiment, 35 other attempts were made with several tens of different antennae, not only in the United States, but also in the Soviet Union, Canada, and France.

After about 5,000 hours of listening from 600 different stars, no artificial message has yet been received. However, this type of research is going on.

Finally, a message lasting three minutes was sent by Americans toward the globular cluster of Hercules with the radio telescope at Arecibo (Puerto Rico). However, since this group of stars is located at a distance of 25,000 light-years away and since radio waves travel at the speed of light, we shall receive a possible answer only in 50,000 years! This figure shows how isolated we are in the vast universe.

Index Numbers in italics refer to illustrations.

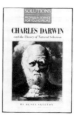
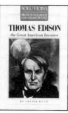
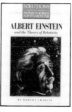